The ABRSM

SONGBOOKPLUS

Grade 1

ABRSM

ABRSM would like to thank the following experts for their valuable contributions to *Songbook Plus*:

Series and singing consultant Eileen Field
Singing consultants Heidi Pegler and John Haythornthwaite
Editorial consultant David Blackwell
Languages consultant Robert Sargant

First published in 2017 by ABRSM (Publishing) Ltd, a wholly owned subsidiary of ABRSM

Reprinted in 2019

Distributed worldwide by Oxford University Press

ISBN 978 1 78601 039 1

AB 3912

Music origination by Julia Bovee
Cover design by Vermillion
Printed in England by Halstan & Co. Ltd, Amersham, Bucks., on materials from sustainable sources.

Contents

This is a selection of the songs from the 2018 Singing syllabus (valid from 1 January 2018 until further notice). For the complete repertoire lists and full details of exam requirements, please see the current syllabus, which should always be referred to for the year in which the exam is to be taken, in case any changes have been made to the requirements: www.abrsm.org/singing.

Notes on the Songs

Notes by Dominic Wells

LIST A

Anna-Marie

This Dutch children's song is a conversation, a series of light-hearted questions and answers between two characters: Anna-Marie and her friend. The questions from Anna-Marie's friend present the same musical material each time, and Anna-Marie's responses have their own musical identity also. However, the dynamics alternate frequently, often from one extreme to another (*f* to *p*, or vice versa), and there is an opportunity for echo singing in the repeated phrases, for example with the friend's opening question at the very beginning. There are also several changes in tempo in the third verse, which concludes with a surprise (delayed) final phrase.

Skye Boat Song

This Scottish folksong, with words by Harold Boulton set to an air collected in the 1870s by Anne MacLeod, recalls the escape of Bonnie Prince Charlie, who disguised himself as a maid and journeyed from South Uist (Outer Hebrides) to the Isle of Skye in a small boat, following the Jacobites' defeat at the Battle of Culloden (1746). The song is often sung as a lullaby, in a slow rocking 6/8 time. In this arrangement the final verse is marked loud, emphasizing the forcefulness of the text, which concludes with a sense of hope that Charlie will one day return.

Go tell it on the mountain

'Go tell it on the mountain' is a spiritual – a type of religious song sung by black slaves in the American South. Dating back to at least 1865 and passed on by oral tradition, it was first written down by John Wesley Work, Jr., the son of a church choir director in Nashville, Tennessee and the first African-American collector of folksongs and spirituals. The song is considered a Christmas carol because the text refers to Jesus's birth, and at Fisk University (where Work taught), early each Christmas morning before sunrise it was customary for students to walk together from building to building singing this song.

LIST B

Sing a Rainbow

'Sing a Rainbow' (also known as 'I Can Sing a Rainbow'), one of the most recognizable and widely sung of children's songs, teaches the colours of the rainbow. It was composed by the American songwriter Arthur Hamilton, best known for his song 'Cry Me a River'. 'Sing a Rainbow' featured in the 1955 film *Pete Kelly's Blues*, but gained greater popularity when it was recorded by the British pop singer Cilla Black in 1966. There are several wide leaps to negotiate, such as the rising 7th between 'a' and 'rainbow', and small differences in the text of the chorus on its second occurrence.

Out in the garden

This song comes from a collection depicting different animals, including an ostrich, an elephant and, of course, Freddie the fly. 'Out in the garden' is about the insects you might find in a garden, told from the perspective of a gnome, who sees all that goes on around him. The nature of some of the insects is described in the alliteration in the text, such as 'slugs slither' and 'honeybees buzz'. The crotchet/minim rhythm in the left hand of the piano resembles the distinctive style of the *Gymnopédies* by the French composer Erik Satie (1866–1925), who also wrote songs about garden creatures.

Susie Hare has written many musicals, songs for schools, and hymns.

Der Abendstern (The Evening Star)

Robert Schumann is one of the most celebrated Romantic composers of piano music and German songs (Lieder). He wrote several pieces about and for children, such as the piano collection *Kinderszenen* ('Scenes from Childhood'). 'Der Abendstern' is one of the 29 songs of *Lieder-Album für die Jugend*, which Schumann wrote specifically for children to perform. The words are directed to a star, shining brightly in the night sky. Source: first edition, *Lieder-Album für die Jugend*, Op. 79 (Leipzig: Breitkopf & Härtel, [1849])

LIST C

We're off to see the wizard

Considered to be one of the greatest American films, *The Wizard of Oz* is a musical fantasy film from 1939, starring Judy Garland as Dorothy. The music was written by Harold Arlen, an American composer of more than 500 popular songs. Many of the film's musical numbers have become very well known, not least 'Over the Rainbow' and this song, 'We're off to see the wizard', which is sung by Dorothy, together with the scarecrow, the tin man and the lion, on their journey to find the wizard.

After the Ball

This melancholic waltz is a popular song written in 1891 by Charles K. Harris. The lines 'many a heart is aching' and 'many the hopes that have vanished' describe the feelings of the character singing: in the little-known verses (not included in this arrangement) he describes seeing his sweetheart kissing another man at a ball, but refuses to listen to her explanation, and years later he discovers that the man was her brother. It is a typical example of sentimental ballads from this time, which often referred to lost love. The expression of the words is reflected in the dynamics, which remain *mf* for the first half, as if the man is resigned to his situation, but then change often – perhaps an expression of his regret.

Conkers!

This is a fun, lively song about collecting the biggest and best conkers, traditionally a popular pastime among children in the autumn, when the leaves are turning golden brown and spiky horse-chestnuts are falling from trees. The song's phrasing is quite distinct in each half: the first part is made up of short phrases but with a longer phrase at the end, while the phrases and notes of the second part ('Under the chestnut tree …') have longer durations, inviting a more sustained, *legato* approach in this section.

Mark and Helen Johnson are the founders and principal songwriters of the music publisher Out of the Ark, which is specifically aimed at music education for children.

Pirates!

The piano begins this song with a brief reference to *The Sailor's Hornpipe* – a traditional melody that immediately conjures up images of sailors dancing on board a ship. The chorus is in two parts with contrasting dynamics: it is quite soft at first, but becomes loud and boisterous for the second half (bar 22). The phrase 'Yo-ho-ho, and a bottle of rum!' has been associated with pirates ever since it appeared as a repeated line in the fictional pirate song 'Dead Man's Chest', in Robert Louis Stevenson's classic novel *Treasure Island* (1883).

Lin Marsh, who has worked extensively in music education and written music for BBC children's programmes, is also a voice specialist, running courses for teachers on singing around the UK and abroad.

Truly Scrumptious

This song is taken from *Chitty Chitty Bang Bang*, a 1968 British musical adventure fantasy film, loosely based on the children's book *Chitty-Chitty-Bang-Bang: The Magical Car* by Ian Fleming (famous for his James Bond spy novels). The film's songs were written by the Sherman Brothers, who composed more musical film scores than any other songwriting team in film history, such as *Mary Poppins* and *The Jungle Book*. Truly Scrumptious (not in the original book) is the daughter of a wealthy sweet factory owner, Lord Scrumptious, and this song is all about her personality and her relationship with the children Jeremy and Jemima Potts, who compare Truly to delicious sweets and treats. The verse has the feel of a children's nursery rhyme.

Catch a falling star

'Catch a falling star' is a pop song made famous by Perry Como, who recorded it in 1957 and won a Grammy Award two years later in the category 'Best Vocal Performance, Male'. It was also the first record certified by the Recording Industry Association of America as 'gold' for selling over a million copies. At this time it was not uncommon for pop songs to be based on pieces of classical music, and the melody of this song is taken from a theme in Brahms's *Academic Festival Overture*. While the rhythm is kept even in the chorus (where the pitches form a palindrome), it is often syncopated in the verse, which contributes to the song's relaxed, good-natured character.

Anna-Marie

Text paraphrased by
Alan Bullard

Trad. Dutch
arr. Alan Bullard

13
That's where I'm go-ing,' said An-na-Ma-rie.
2. 'And
17
where are you off to now, An-na-Ma-rie?
And where are you off to now, An-na-Ma rie?'
21
'Down to the sea-side to swim in the sea,
That's where I'm off to,' said An-na-Ma-rie.
25
'Down to the sea-side to swim in the sea,
That's where I'm off to,' said An-na-Ma-rie.

Slower and freely
29
rit.
mf
f
3. 'Now, where are you go-ing to, An-na-Ma-rie? Now,
p
mf
Tempo primo
33
rit.
p
where are you go-ing to, An-na-Ma-rie?' 'Back where I start-ed, to fin-ish my tea,
f
p
accel. al fine
37
f
That's where I'm go-ing,' said An-na-Ma-rie. 'Back where I start-ed, to
f
40
ff
fin-ish my tea, That's where I'm go-ing,' said An-na-Ma-rie!
optional 15ma
ff

Skye Boat Song

Harold Boulton
(1859–1935)

for me: straight through

Trad. Scottish
collected and adapted by Anne MacLeod
(1855–1921)
arr. Nancy Litten

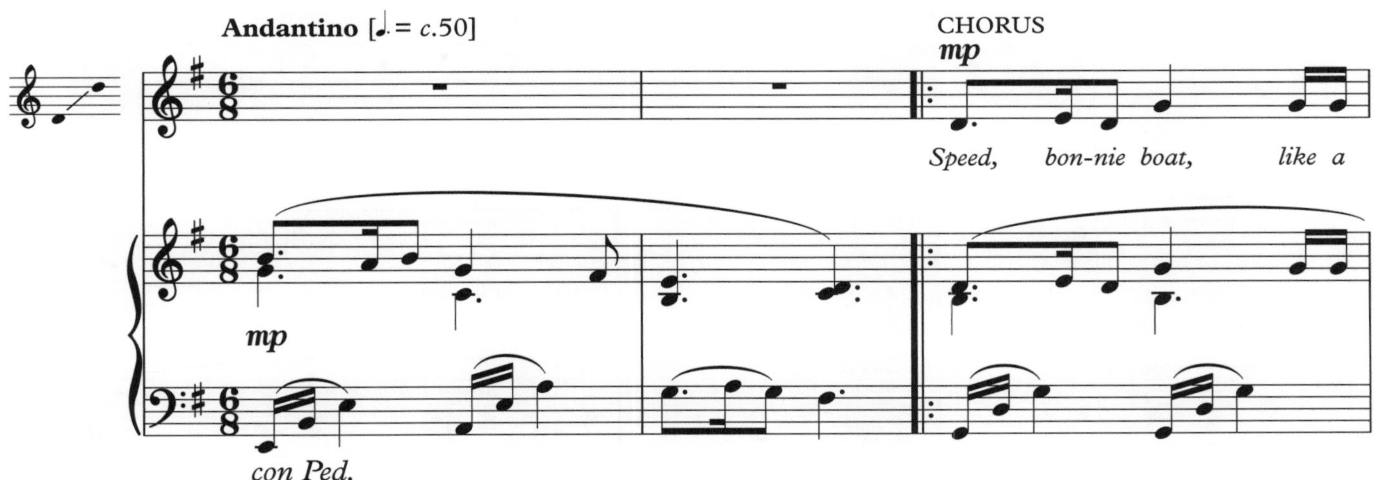

11
f 1. Loud the winds howl, loud the waves roar, Thun-der-claps rend the air;
mf 3. Ma-ny's the lad fought on that day, Well the clay-more could wield,
f (mf)
15
Baf-fled, our foes stand by the shore, Fol-low they will not dare.
mp When the night came, si-lent-ly lay Dead on Cul-lo-den's field.
(mp)
CHORUS
19
mf
Speed, bon-nie boat, like a bird on the wing, On-ward! The sail-ors cry;
mf
23
Car-ry the lad that's born to be King O-ver the sea to Skye.

27
mp 2. Though the waves leap, soft shall ye sleep, O-cean's a roy - al bed.
f 4. Burned are our homes, ex - ile and death Scat-ter the loy - al men;
mp (f)
31
Rocked in the deep, Flo-ra will keep Watch by your wea - ry head.
Yet ere the sword cool in the sheath Char-lie will come a - gain.
CHORUS
35
f
Speed, bon-nie boat, like a bird on the wing, On - ward! The sail - ors cry;
f
39
mf
rit.
p
Car - ry the lad that's born to be King O - ver the sea to Skye.
mf
p
Ped.

Go tell it on the mountain

Trad. Spiritual

arr. Nikki Iles

11
mf
shep - herds kept their watch - ing o'er si - lent flocks by night, Be -
shep - herds feared and trem - bled when lo! a - bove the earth, Rang
in a low - ly man - ger the hum - ble Christ was born, And
mp
mf
15
1.2.
3.
- hold through - out the hea - vens there shone a ho - ly light.
out the an - gel cho - rus that hailed our Sa - viour's birth.
God sent out sal - va - tion that bless - ed Christ - mas morn.
19
CHORUS
Go tell it on the moun - tain, o - ver the hills and ev - er - y - where.
23
slight rall.
mp
Go tell it on the moun - tain that Je - sus Christ is born.
mp
p

Sing a Rainbow

from *Pete Kelly's Blues*

Words and music by
Arthur Hamilton
(born 1926)

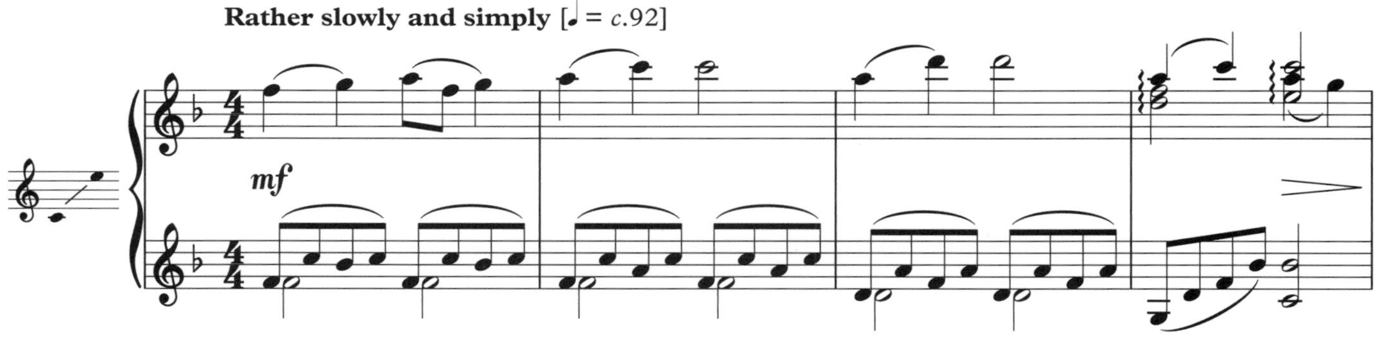

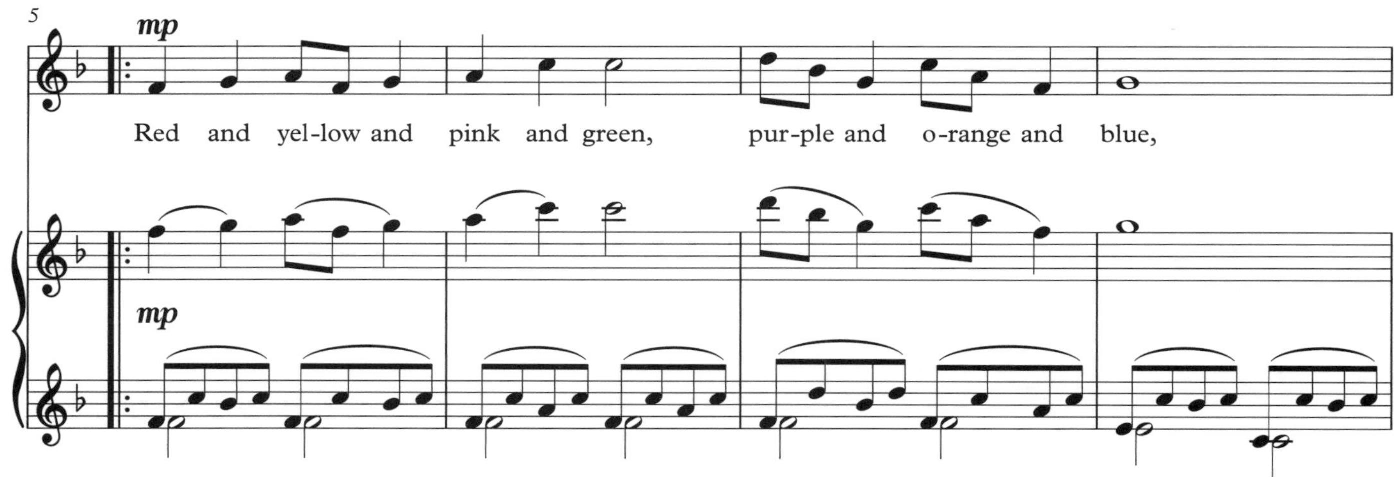

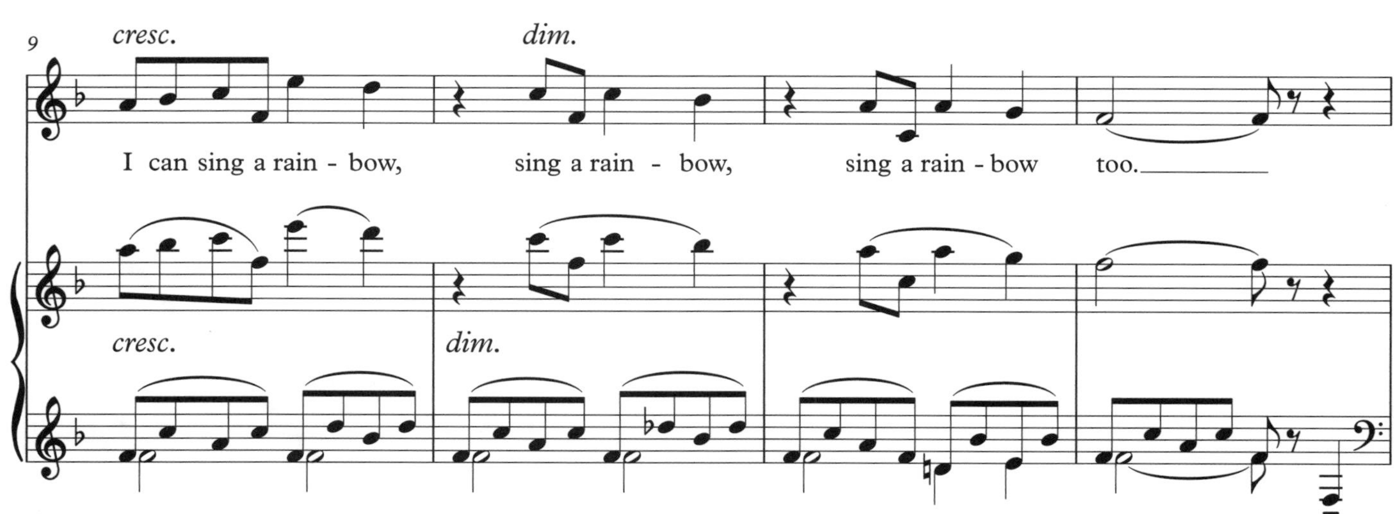

13
mf
Lis-ten with your eyes, lis - ten with your eyes and sing ev-'ry-thing you see.
mf
17
You can sing a rain-bow, sing a rain-bow, sing a-long with me.
p
Red and yel-low and
p
22
pink and green, pur-ple and o-range and blue.
cresc.
Now we can sing a rain - bow,
f
cresc.
f
26
mf
sing a rain - bow, sing a rain - bow too. too.
p
1.
2.
poco rit.
pp
mf
p
pp

Out in the garden

No. 8 from *Freddie the Fly*

Words and music by
Susie Hare
(born 1947)

4. Out in the garden where the gard'ners potter,
so many tiny creatures make their home.
Some like it cool and some like it hotter.
I never mind 'cos I'm the garden gnome.

Der Abendstern

The Evening Star

No. 1 from *Lieder-Album für die Jugend*, Op. 79

Hoffmann von Fallersleben
(1798–1874)
English words by
Heidi Pegler

Robert Schumann
(1810–56)
ed. Heidi Pegler

p
9
3. So blick' ich nach dir, sei's dort o - der hier: dein
So each brand new day, I heart - i - ly pray You
4. Wie nickst du mir zu in fröh - li - cher Ruh'! O
You shine joy - ous - ly, And set my heart free, O
p

13
freund - li - ches Äug - lein steht im - mer vor mir.
twin - kle so bright - ly and show me the way.
lieb - li - ches Stern - lein, o wär' ich wie du!
star glow - ing bright - ly re - main close to me.

We're off to see the wizard

from *The Wizard of Oz*

E. Y. Harburg
(1896–1981)

Harold Arlen
(1905–86)

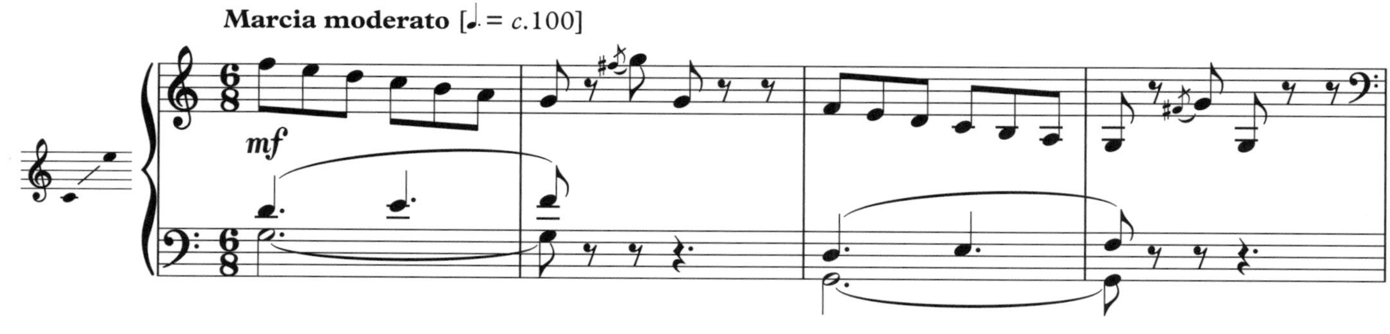

13
Fol - low, fol - low, fol - low, fol - low, Fol - low the yel - low brick
16
road.
Fol - low the rain - bow o - ver the stream,
19
Fol - low the fel - low who fol - lows a dream,
Fol - low, fol - low,
22
fol - low, fol - low, Fol - low the yel - low brick road.
CHORUS
We're

25
mf
off to see the Wiz - ard, The won-der-ful Wiz-ard of Oz. We
mf
29
hear he is a whiz of a Wiz if ev - er a Wiz there was. If
33
ev - er, oh ev - er a Wiz there was, The Wiz-ard of Oz is one be - coz, be -
37
- coz, be - coz, be - coz, be - coz, be - coz, Be -

41
-coz of the won-der-ful things he does.
We're
45
off to see the Wiz-ard, The won-der-ful Wiz-ard of Oz.
1.
mf
49a
We're
48b
2.
Oz.
mf

After the Ball

Words and music by
Charles K. Harris
(1865/7–1930)
arr. David Blackwell

Waltz tempo [♩ = *c*.144]

15
leav - ing, Af - ter the stars are gone;
21
mp
Ma - ny a heart is ach - ing, If you could read them
cresc.
27
all;
mf
Ma - ny the hopes that have van - ished,
33
1.
2.
f
Af - ter the ball.
ball.

Conkers!

from *Songs for Every Season*

Words and music by
Mark Johnson (born 1957)
and Helen Johnson (born 1964)

20
1. Un - der the chest - nut tree, there waits for me, a
2. Un - der the chest - nut tree, where no - one's been, the
3. Un - der the chest - nut tree, I stretch to see, a
25
sight so marv'- llous to be - hold. A - midst the au - tumn
spi - ky shells lie on the ground. Be - neath their ar - mour
fi - nal con - ker to be mine. If I can on - ly
30
leaves, it gleams at me, a con - ker, beau - ti - ful and
green, there hides un - seen, a con - ker, smooth and shi - ny
reach, to pull it free, I'll add it to my nine - ty -
35a
1.2.
3.
(shouted)
D.S. al Coda
bold.
brown.
- nine! ONE HUN - DRED!
CODA
rest!

Pirates!

Words and music by
Lin Marsh
(born 1950)

14
skull and cross - bones on the mast, a wild and noi - sy crew: the
mp
18
pi - rate ship is com - ing and it's af - ter me and you!
22
f
Yo - ho - ho and a bot - tle of rum, pi - rates like to have their fun!
f
26
1.2.
3.
Yo - ho - ho on the 'Sal - ty Breeze' as they sail the se - ven seas.
seas.
mf

Truly Scrumptious

from *Chitty Chitty Bang Bang*

Words and music by
Richard M. Sherman (born 1928)
and Robert B. Sherman (1925–2012)

13
Su-gar plum, cin-na-mon and le - mon tart, tell you what they are right from the start. And
17
your name does the same for you, by co-in - ci-dence:
a tempo – Broadly
CHORUS
21
mf
(Children) 1. Tru - ly Scrump-tious; you're tru - ly, tru - ly scrump - tious;
(Truly) 2. Tru - ly scrump-tious; you two are tru - ly scrump - tious;
mf
25
scrump-tious as a cher - ry peach par - fait.
scrump-tious as the breeze a - cross the bay.

29
When you're near me, it's so de - li - cious;
When you're smil - ing, it's so de - li - cious;
33
hon - est, Tru - ly, you're the an - swer to my wish - es.
so be - guil - ing; you're the an - swer to my wish - es.
37
Tru - ly Scrump - tious, though I may seem 'pre - sump - tious',
Tru - ly scrump - tious, you two are tru - ly scrump - tious,
41
nev - er, nev - er ev - er go a - way.
and I shan't for - get this love - ly day.

45
My heart beats so un - ru - ly, be - cause I love you tru - ly,
My heart beats so un - ru - ly, I al - so love you tru - ly,

49
1.
hon - est, Tru - ly, I do.
hon - est, Tru - ly, I
NO

51b
2.
rit.
do.
then give
E A

Exam requirements: omitting verse 2; low g's may be sung an octave higher

Catch a falling star

Paul J. Vance
(born 1929)

Lee Pockriss
(1924–2011)

13
love may come and tap___ you on the shoul-der
when your trou-bles start___ in mul-ti-ply-ing,
Some star-less night.
And they just might.
And
It's
mf
17
2nd time D.S. al Coda
just in case you feel___ you want to hold her,
eas-y to for-get___ them with-out try-ing,
You'll have a pock-et full of star-light.
With just a pock-et full of star-light.
CODA
21
day.
Save it for a rain-y day.
Save it for a
25
rain-y day.
poco a poco morendo